Stories and prayers by
# Hilary Faith Jones

# Milestones

with illustrations by **Eddie Askew**

By the same author:

*Awakenings*
*Waiting for Jesus*
*The Wonderful Picnic*

Published by The Leprosy Mission International
80 Windmill Road, Brentford, Middlesex TW8 0QH, United Kingdom

First published 2004
© Stories and Prayers Hilary Faith Jones
© Illustrations A. D. (Eddie) Askew

Hilary Faith Jones has asserted her right to be identified as the author of this work in accordance with the Copyright, Designs and Patents Act 1988.

*All rights and subsidiary rights have been granted to*
*The Leprosy Mission International (see page 112 for contact details).*

*Editorial and Design by Craft Plus Publishing Ltd.*
*53 Crown Street, Brentwood, Essex CM14 4BD*

Printed and bound in Malta by Gutenberg Press Limited
A catalogue record for this book is available from the British Library.
ISBN 0 902731 51 3

Cover picture and title page (printed in full on page 47):
Spring Flowers, Mount Carmel, *Watercolour*
Picture page 2: Resting, *Watercolour*
Picture page 5: Summer Meadow, *Watercolour*

*For Stef, the truest of friends*
*and for Stephen, who transforms my life*

# Foreword

Five years ago I was laid up in bed. At least I could do some reading. I picked up a manuscript entitled *Awakenings* by one Hilary Faith Jones. I started to read and didn't stop until I'd finished. This was good, very good. Hilary knew how to write; her words resonated in me, sparking my imagination into life. I felt the tears, desperation, loss, rejection and then the hope, joy, glory and power described in her stories. We must publish this as soon as possible. In the last five years TLM Trading Limited, The Leprosy Mission's trading company, has sold over 20,000 copies of *Awakenings*. Not bad for a first book from someone previously unknown in the publishing world. Hilary followed *Awakenings* with *Waiting for Jesus* published in 2001. The profits from both of these books have been used to help those affected by leprosy.

The years have passed, and yes, I'm laid up in bed again! That's the bad news. The good news is that I have the manuscript of Hilary's third book *Milestones* and it is certainly another winner. Hilary's writing is vivid, thought provoking and inspired. Her writing helps our imaginations to glimpse the glory and majesty, the power and love of our God and Saviour. She challenges us to take a second look at well-known Bible stories and to really think about how it must have felt to be there, to hear Jesus' voice, to witness the event or to wonder at the miracle. Hilary includes some very powerful and gritty stories – the stoning of Stephen, Judas' suicide. She encourages us to examine these stories and to ask ourselves what might have happened next.

Read this book and experience a master storyteller at work. Lend it to people on the edge of the Christian faith as an invitation to come in and explore a little more. Writers with a gift like Hilary's are rare and precious.

Happy reading!

*Noel Jones*

Chief Executive, TLM Trading Limited. January 2004

# Introduction

There are many great turning points in life which profoundly change us.

This book tells stories of people in the Bible who encounter Jesus at major moments in their life. Some of the encounters are at the most joyous and wondrous moments, some are at the darkest and most frightening times. Some, like marriage, are willingly chosen, and others, like bereavement, are unavoidable. Just so in our lives, we face similar turning points.

It would be wrong to concentrate purely on the lovely and the good and the wholesome experiences, for life is not like that, which is why I have included stories about bereavement and martyrdom.

Suicide though, is one of life's most contentious and heart-breaking issues. There is no Biblical evidence for the story written about Judas. It is purely creative writing but I felt it was important to include it, even if it only prompts us to question.

I have also included a story called *The Dance*. Did Jesus ever dance? The Bible does not mention dancing, but there again it does not mention Jesus laughing or hugging his mother. Yet was Christ not fully human and fully divine?

So *Milestones* was written, inspired deeply by those I love, my family and friends. I pray that it will bring you much inspiration as you encounter your next milestone.

*Hilary faith Jones*

Hilary Faith Jones
January 2004

# Bible references

# Contents

# Letting Go

The bills were paid,
bags strapped to patient donkeys,
shouts of greetings and departures filled the air.
Landlords clasped their lodgers' hands and wished them
God's speed until they came again.
And the roads around Jerusalem began to fill
as early marketers inward trundled
against the steady stream of visitors homeward bound.

Apart from missing the children she loved it all.
The preparations, the long journey,
the excitement of returning each year to the holy centre.
The pleasure of sharing holy days with the family –
the vast number of relatives and close friends,
the time set aside each year
to catch up on everyone's life,
their events since last meeting,
their hopes and plans for the next year.
Such a special time –
this great coming together for Passover.
The celebration of God, of each other,
of being drawn together because of the bond of faith.

And this Passover had been even more special
for their eldest child was now twelve
and old enough to accompany them.
And watching Him absorb, question,
understand at such a rate, opened her eyes.
She felt as if she was seeing it all afresh –
the city, the great Temple, the argued debates –
all became new and strange and exciting
as she watched it through the eyes of her son.

The dust rose and hung in heavy clouds over the road.
Once clear of the city's gates,
the crowd thinned and dispersed allowing space to breathe and think.
She pulled loose the shawl and let the wind blow through her hair.
Felt deep happiness run through her.
They were going home and it had been a truly wonderful time.

It wasn't until evening that they re-grouped at a wayside inn.
She looked around,

> *I can't see him, Joseph.*

Her husband felt the ground move under him.
Catching her worry he strode quickly to the back buildings
but found only the tired husbands unloading the animals for the night.
No sign of an eager, laughing child.

The father went from one to another.

> *When did you last see my son?*
> *I thought he was travelling with you.*

And the sickening reply,

> *Sorry, we presumed he'd fallen back to stay with you today.*

She took one look at his ashen face and knew.

> *O God help us – he's so young. What have we done, Joseph?*
>
> *I'll go straight back to Jerusalem.*
> *He'll have had the sense to stay there when he couldn't find us.*

He flung the bags together.

She spoke calmly,
trying to push down the rising tide of panic inside.

> *I'm coming with you. If we move quickly we could*
> *be back to the lodgings before they shut.*
> *If he's not there …* her voice broke … *He's so vulnerable, so alone …*

Within minutes they were off,
the anxious prayers of the party called after them
in the rapidly falling dark.
They didn't speak,
saving their breath to push on further,
arriving back at the Jerusalem lodgings
only to have their hopes dashed.
The landlord was immediately sympathetic
reading in their distraught faces the unspoken fear,
but he could be of little comfort
other than giving them food and warmth.
So the night stretched on relentlessly
while they waited sleepless for dawn to come.

Not once in all the long hours of the days that followed,
did they stop praying.
Whispered prayers again and again in their hearts as they trod
the warm stones
stopping, asking, begging at every corner,
every street seller,
every familiar sight.

> *Have you seen a boy? About this tall?*
> *Strong for his age but oh, so very trusting.*

> *O God ... the mother whispered again and again,*
> *... too trusting, too unaware.*
> *We should have taught him differently.*
> *Forgive me Lord. Forgive me.*

And again and again,
as she ran down alleyways and pushed
through bright awnings and searched dark doorways,
she bargained with God,

> *My life for his, God.*
> *Please, please just let me find him,*
> *whole and safe.*

*O God, don't abandon me now.*
*Please, God, please, please, God.*

Until,
worn down by fear and broken by loss
the dawning of the third day saw them wearily climbing the Temple steps,
as they had twelve years earlier.
But this time there was no babe in arms,
no loving protection to surround the child.
The pain shot through her
and she leaned heavily against Joseph,
her body heaving,
wracked with the agony of breathing unshed tears.

And, as if by some strange trick of mind,
she heard His voice –
clear and strong on the morning air,
as gentle and powerful as when he spoke seriously with his friends.
The parents stared, mesmerised,
unsure whether their desperate need had created an illusion.

Slowly the father walked on,
stepped amongst the great teachers and philosophers,
the students and the priests,
and came to stand behind his son.
He waited, breathless, for the boy to finish speaking,
then put his hand upon the child's arm.
Feeling his touch
the boy turned and His face lit with love.
He flung his arms around His father's neck
and held onto him.

> *I'm so glad you've come,* He said, His face shining,
> *I so wanted you to share.*

Joseph slowly took in the crowd of the greatest minds
listening reverently to his child.

He spoke gently,

> *Your mother is anxious.*
> *She is here too!* exclaimed the boy,
> and ran through the assembly
> laughing with delight into His mother's arms.

Sobbing, she held Him against her,
kissing His hair, His face, His hands.

> *We were so desperately worried.*

He touched the tears that soaked her cheeks
and answered with all the forthright clarity of youth.

> *Where else in all the world would I be*
> *except here,* and He flung His arms wide, *in my father's house.*

And with a sudden rush of fear
his mother realised He was no longer a child.
He needed the intellects and the great theologians,
needed the excitement of discovering God-in-others,
needed to be set free.
And her heart ached differently inside her.

They started the journey home,
the boy running ahead
his non-stop chatter drifting back to them.
These last moments of childhood
were suddenly infinitely precious.

They both knew,
the God-boy had heard the calling of the world
and was leaving childhood behind.
For he understood the eternal source,
was inextricably part of God,
belonged to that mystery
at which they could only kneel and worship.

Watching Him,
they felt awestruck that they had been chosen.
But then,
they also felt torn,
for they loved Him as parents love.
And they had known instinctively that, as He grew up,
He needed to be held in the warmth of their arms,
needed to know what it was like
to be swung through the air onto His father's shoulders,
needed the rough and tumble of the little ones,
to hold their chubby fingers and guide them in their first steps.
He needed to know the all encompassing power – and pain – of love.

But now
He was stepping out of the home
that they had given Him.
And letting go
was unbearably,
unspeakably hard.

But then the wind blew round them.
And, feeling the touch of God,
they turned to face the warmth of the sun.

And Joseph smiled as they breathed in God.
He drew his wife to him.

> *This impossible, bewildering,*
> *deeply-loving boy*
> *will transform more lives than just ours.*

She held his hand very tightly.
And together
they watched the silhouette of the boy
as He ran forward into the glory of the sun.

Is it not through love
that we learn to soar like eagles,
flying on open wings through storm and light?

Is it not through love
that we learn to lift our eyes
and fill the air with the laughter of our song?

Is it not through love
that we discover who we are
and wonder at the brilliance of our being?

Is it not through love
that we discover Christ
and learn to live with risk?

Is it not through love
that God is clearest seen?

Amen I therefore say.
Amen to Christ.
And Amen to love.

City Walls, Jerusalem
*Watercolour*

# Into Baptism

Hot giggles burst out of the child,
rising into the morning air like a crescendo of bird-flight,
making his mother smile
in her gentle and perpetual struggle to dress and feed him.

His eyes were transfixed by the movement of the leaves outside.
The door swung slightly in the breeze –
and his attention was caught.
Bare feet pushing away his elderly father,
he pulled the door open
and ran into the endless day.

He scrabbled fearlessly over huge rocks,
peering into the silent overhangs,
hiding in dark crevasses,
the cool seeping into him.
Rolling over and over in delight
between light and dark,
cold shadows and scorching sun.
Lying on the ground,
fingers exploring the recesses and cracks in the baked earth,
fascinated by the insects that darted
unharmed across his skin,
minutely absorbing the intricacies of tiny armour,
the hardness of the stones,
the slicing of sharp leaves across the sky.

Free.
One.

With the falling of the dusk
his parents searched for him,
knowing that he would not be at other children's homes
for he was not one of them.
Calling for him instead amongst the barren rocks and windswept plains.

And when found
the old man would lift him carefully,
soothing the damp hair away from his sleeping face,
slowly stepping home
with the increasing weight of the responsibility of this
strange child.

Yet,
he was their unspoken gift.

He was born, created, different.
They knew that he would never fit into society.
He would break all conventions and rules,
so fierce was his spirit.

And they did not want him
to be broken.
Exhausting, unruly, unpredictable,
but he brought them
into a different discovery of God.

Hurtling through the unchecked storms that swept land and skies,
he grew.
Bursting now with questions.
The why and when and how,
where, what and but,
resounding amongst the outcrops,
beating into the earth.

Sometimes just to sit,
motionless.
Still with being,
the hours slipping by unnoticed.
Held by the faith of the old
the vastness of God developed unhindered in his mind,
until he seemed to burn
like a small star amongst the rocky slopes.

————

Until some years later,
having grown unfettered,
he was appalled by restrictions binding religious rituals.
This was not the God he knew.

Climbing onto precipitous ledges, the man of the wild stood
swaying against the wind,
thoughts tumbling over and over.

> *I can hear it.*
> *In every fibre of every leaf,*
> *inside every stone and living creature.*
> *The air is singing with it.*
> *You are present.*
> *Here.*
> *Somewhere.*
> *Walking.*
> *Waiting.*
> *Sleeping.*
> *One of us.*

He crouched down, buffeted.
Wrapping his arms around his knees.

> *Cities are packed with religion —*
> *yet so lacking in You, Lord —*
> *just being fed scraps of a ritualised God.*

*Why?* he cried out to the wind that snatched his voice.

*Why do they not see?*
*So desperately unprepared.*
*So aimless.*
*O God!*

… he rocked harder on his heels.

*They're not ready –*
*they'll miss the signs.*

The sun vanished and dark settled.
He stood on the precipice,
his toes curled over the edge,
poised like an eagle before flight.
Perfect balance over the dark folds of the land.


And sweeping up from the vast expanse of spreading night,
he heard what he waited for.

*Prepare the Way!*

An enormous soul-filling cry erupted from his throat
soaring across the landscape.
A call tinged with wilderness.
Waking, summoning, demanding.


It was what the people had been waiting for.
As days turned into months
the call echoed on.
Not fading,
but gaining power.
Until it became
like a great wave,
sweeping across the land.

Startled and wondrous
the people travelled to him,
longing to catch something of his charisma,
to be touched by his intensity for God.

Not belonging to society,
he had no time for rules or politicking or games.
So he knew no fear.
Thin and taut,
he whipped back at the questioners,
thundering down those who held power through hypocrisy,
moving deeply into the heart of those who held unpopular jobs
yet longed for God.

> *Ask for forgiveness.*
> *It will be given to you.*
> *Start anew.*

Exasperated by the repeated murmurings that he was the Christ,
he shouted,

> *No!*

turning and running to the river.

> *Look!*

He flung the water into great sweeping arcs.

> *I baptise with water.*
> *It's symbolic – the washing away of the past,*
> *a physical, spiritual new beginning.*
> *But the Christ will baptise with fire.*
> *Set your soul alight.*
> *Fill you with the Holy Spirit.*
> *You **must** be ready.*
> *Begin anew.*

And suddenly they were up on their feet,
running towards him,
faces full of hope,
laughter and cries filling the air as they splashed through the water.
Desperately reaching out to be ready for God.
Line after line,
day after day.

Until one afternoon ...

He had woken that morning worn out.
Tired.
Those that clustered around him attracted by his outspoken challenge to authority,
needed more than he could give them.
He did not speak the language of men.
He could not feed their searching and questing.
He simply was not one of them.
And for a moment,
he had longed to be a child again.
Uncomplicated.
Running through the desert waiting for his father
to find him.

With the queue stretching back to the bank,
he stood waist-deep in the eddying river;
bare feet firmly gripping the stony river-bed,
his thin, wiry body swaying with the water currents,
when instantly he was jolted into the immediate.
The man in front of him, smiling at him,
was his cousin.

He stopped,
hand in mid-air,
the water splashing through his fingers.

     *Jesus!*

Delight and bewilderment held him in surprise.

     *Baptise me.*

The Baptiser stared,
his thoughts in disarray.

     *Baptise me.* Jesus said again.

Immediately he swept the water over his cousin's head.

     *Jesus – I* ... he began,

when suddenly the force of thunder ripping through the clouds
nearly lifted him off his feet.

The air around sparked furiously
as if the very particles of existence
were being ignited.
The waters heaved and raced towards them,
everything in him that was of the wild became frenzied,
his very blood seemed to be scorching –
caught into the tremendous outpouring of energy
that was flooding sky and earth.

As if in slow motion,
the forerunner turned in awe to his cousin.
For a moment
his startled eyes met the Christ's –
so like him and yet
with a deepness of something the forerunner
had only ever caught a glimpse.

And then the Christ lifted His head further back
to open His face to the endless skies,
as the air filled with the brilliance of fission,
and the eternity of the sky split in two.
And the wild one caught his breath
as he gazed into the heart of the eternal source.

So wondrous,
so powerful,
so beyond the greatest mind.
Soul-stirring.

The Christ, his cousin, this crowd-man
leant further back,
laughing with delight,
His arms reaching up to embrace the out-pouring;
freed for a moment from humanity.
Reunited.

And quite clearly
the witness to this union heard God speak
in human voice so he would understand.

>    *My beloved Son, with whom I am well pleased.*

And the unschooled one
closed his eyes as he felt the terrible power of the wind rush towards them,
instinctively protecting his face
at the pounding of wings.
But then only tenderness touched his cheek
as fragile as the feather
of a dove.

And his hand was taken from his face
by the Christ.

> *My brother,*
> *my friend.*
> *Do not be afraid.*

The forerunner held on to the solid reality of the hand,
human warmth from flesh and bone,
and forced his eyes open.
Although the air was faintly humming,
the sky was unclouding
and the waters had quietened;
order had been restored.
It was as before.
The queue still stretched back patiently
to the bank.

This Christ was his life –
this God-in-Man.
And now that He was here
there was so much he wanted to say
but he did not know the words.

> *Why?*
> *I mean how …?*
> *No, I mean you shouldn't be like them …*

Baptism of forgiveness –
man coming to God.
Yet, this was more.
Baptism of blessing.
An offering.
God coming to man.

He clutched the hand fiercely.

>    *I'm not worthy of you,* he whispered.

But the God-in-Man,
the one who had come out from the crowd,
gathered him to Himself
and kissed him strongly on the forehead.

>    *You have run magnificently for me.*

He held him tight for a moment
and then was gone,
a figure swallowed immediately by the crowd.

In growing amazement,
stunned wonder,
the forerunner gazed after Him,
trying to distinguish Him in the mass of people.

And then he felt an overwhelming power fill
the air again –
achingly beautiful,
wild and fierce,
heart-breakingly tender.

Deepening into awe,
he surrendered to love.
With soul soaring he turned back to those who waited.

A.D. ASKEW

*Pure water.*
*Infinity and light.*
*Breaking over my emptiness.*
*I come to You my God.*

*Celestial fire.*
*Divinity of Spirit.*
*Transforming my brokenness.*
*You come to me O God.*

*And the desert of my being*
*flowers into the vivacity of life.*

Aysgarth Falls, Yorkshire
*Pastel*

# The Calling

The late afternoon was settling into evening.
The fisherman paused for a moment to raise
his eyes to the long shadowed hills
before running his hands,
made huge from salt soaking,
over the keel of his boat.

He swung on board
and began to carefully work his way through
the nets.
Slow.
Sure.
With a child-like gentleness that sometimes belongs to massive men.

*Simon?*

He glanced up,
pushing the heavy hair out of his eyes and studied his younger brother.
He knew his every gesture, every intonation.
Knew his dreams and hopes,
his thoughts and questions.
His faith.
He'd seen that look on his face before,
usually as they sailed home in the dawn,
the boat skimming the waters,
eyes brimming with sea and sky.

He left the nets
and dropped over into the sea.

*What's up?*

*I want you to see someone.*

*Oh aye?* He stopped to wash the grease off his hands.
*Friend of the Baptiser's?*

He liked John.
Liked the roughness and the rawness of him.
Liked the way he disturbed people,
made them think.
Sometimes after a night's work,
they would stop off by the river
and sit on the banks listening to him.

And on quiet nights,
when the fishing was slow and the wind had dropped,
then his brother would talk of the new ideas,
the new ways that the Baptiser was teaching.
And he would listen,
occasionally questioning,
letting the different thoughts linger unbroken.
Then it was
that their partner boat would draw near.
And intrigued,
the other John, with his brother James,
would sit astride the side closest,
and they would argue and laugh with Andrew,
and fall quiet in their hunger to know more.
And the thinking of the four men
would rest upon the dark waters.

*It's his cousin,* Andrew replied.

*What's he like?*

There was a moment's hesitation,
not from uncertainty,
but from the importance of what he needed to say.

*I think he might be the Messiah.*

Andrew's eyes did not move from his brother's face.

*That's why I want you to meet him.*

Simon straightened up and studied his brother for a long time.
He knew he had been deeply
influenced by the Baptiser —
but this was different.


When your livelihood was as hard
and as dangerous as theirs,
you learnt to know human nature.
You learnt to sense the intangible.
He and Andrew,
indeed James and John,
trusted their lives to each other every day.
He knew his brother spoke the truth.

———


They found the house
and suddenly Simon hesitated.
This was ridiculous,
of course it couldn't be true.
Andrew smiled at him
as he led the way through to the courtyard.

*Jesus — I've brought my brother!*

The yard was warm.
Red plants splashed brilliantly against walls.
Children and dogs filled the air with delighted shrieks
as they chased in and out of the doorways;
whilst in the centre, resting around low tables,
guests were freely talking with the women.
They had arrived at a moment of spontaneity.
Everyone was relaxed and immensely happy —
like the very best times in a family reunion.

Hearing Andrew's voice,
the group turned to welcome them.
And a man nearly as tall as Simon,
but without his massive breadth,
came forward,
still laughing from some remark just made.

He held out His hand to Simon
and the great fisherman –
whose hands could crush the jaws of an eel –
found himself in a grip beyond any he had experienced.

Surprised,
he looked more keenly into the face of the man
and drew his breath in sharply –
for fleetingly he glimpsed something vast.
Momentous.
But then the insight was gone,
a fragment that slipped out of his thoughts,
for the man was smiling at him.

> *So you are Simon?*

He indicated the handclasp.

> *From now on, you will be Peter.*
> *The rock.*
> *Come and sit with us.*

It was an evening that rocked his thoughts.
At one moment, it was as if he was talking to his best friend –
his brother, or James or John;
without reserve,
each knowing and understanding the past of the other.
And then at the next,
it was as if he was witnessing some
glorious divine presence.

Once, one of the children leaning against Jesus
interrupted and asked Him to explain –
and smiling, He had taken the child on His knee
and spoken of God so simply, so heart-movingly,
that it was as if great shafts of light
were breaking through the austere image of
the Almighty that they had grown up with.

Simon Peter felt the strangest sensation of being complete.
Normally not given to talking about his faith,
he found himself talking about God.
God in the power of the sea-storms
and within the pounding fear of your heart.
God in the cry of the gulls bringing them home through
the mists.
God in the toil and sweat and strain of human sinews
and aching muscles.
God in his home, in his wife, in his children.
A God of reality.
At the heart of his existence.

The words flowed from him.
A beautiful song of poetry.
Suddenly embarrassed, he stopped.
Smiled lopsidedly at Jesus.
Jesus nodded at him.

> *Well spoken my friend,* He said gently.

That night –
and the next and the next –
Andrew and he sat on the boat talking long hours about the man, Jesus.
Times of deep thought.

They did not know,
but it was a transitional time.
The space between the past and the future.

James and John drew alongside.
Listening, occasionally questioning,
their hands working absent-mindedly over the catch,
feeling the awesomeness of change in the night air.

It seemed to them all
that this man had opened God to them.
It was quite extraordinary.
God was physically present,
reaching out to them.

They were men of the seas.
By their very nature they accepted unfathomable
mysteries in a way that great intellects could not;
they knew that there was a time beyond assurances
when one moved in faith;
they were men who had spent their lives
watching the midnight skies,
letting the wind and sea guide them.

They felt now that same magnetism that
guided them through nature,
guiding them to this man.

But it was a thousand times stronger.
They knew,
without words,
deep down in the burning of their hearts,
that this was God –
calling to them.

Simon Peter wanted Jesus to know his family,
to be a part of all that he was.
Especially as this was a bad time;
his mother-in-law sick with fever and the
fear of death etched over his wife's face.

Within minutes of His arrival,
his wife, normally reserved in front of strangers,
was pouring out her heart to Him;
clutching His hands within hers,
the words tumbling out of her.

And He understood,
had quietly sat beside her mother,
His hands drawing heat from her
until, healed, she rose.
At peace,
tinged with the beauty of age.

That night,
Simon Peter stayed home.
He needed to talk with his family.
And especially with his wife.
Finally, in the darkest hours,
he sighed and sat on the edge of his mattress.
Bowed his head between his hands.

Beside him, his wife turned her head and watched him,
knowing his turmoil, feeling it in his breathing, his restlessness.
She knelt up and wrapped her arms around him,
resting her head against the taut muscles of his back.
Just like when they were young.
He smiled in the dark.

It was the most life-changing decision that they had to face.
Finally she spoke.

> *If he asks,*
> *you must go.*

As she spoke, he laid his hands over hers.

*My gentle darling,*
*your heart is so big.*
*He will be able to work great things through you.*
*And …*

she paused.

*I think he needs you.*

His voice seemed to be caught in his throat.
He had difficulty speaking.

*And you?*

She was silent for a long time.
Turning,
he realised her cheeks were wet with tears.

*My love for you will never grow old.*
*It will not diminish with time*
*or grow faint with distance,*
*but continue to grow richer and deeper.*

He gave a great sob as she continued.

*Even though I cannot be there –*
*my heart is with you –*
*every step of the journey.*

Turning he took her in his arms and held her very close.

The morning that He came for them followed one of the most
startlingly beautiful nights.
Hearing a shoal leaping through the inshore currents,
he and Andrew brought the boat in closer.
And there was Jesus.
Waiting.
His voice
deep and joyous
carried clearly on the early air.
Calling to them.

So it was
that the three of them pulled the boat in,
laughing and talking.
And they knew what He would ask.
And they knew what they would answer.

> *Follow me.*

Simon Peter's heart leaped with unbelievable happiness.
He held out his hands.

> *We will follow you Jesus.*
> *Right to the very end … and beyond.*

And for a fraction of a second,
he became acutely aware of the creaking
of the boat's timbers beside him.
But then Jesus smiled and held out His arms to embrace them.

They walked for the last time along the shore.
Past James and John who watched them silently,
their eyes following after them,
knowing they were leaving.

Simon Peter hesitated and looked at Jesus:

Jesus read his question,
then turned and called,

> *James and John.*
> *Come with me!*

Their shouts of delight could be heard
echoing amongst the rocks
as they heaved through the waters,
laughing and yelling with resounding exuberance,
as they raced up to join them.

Simon Peter caught Jesus' glance,

> *I know – they're not quiet,* he murmured.

> *Sons of thunder!* Jesus laughed.

The first four.
Rough.
Strong.
Faithful.
True.

Men who knew how to serve each other.
Work for each other.
Die for each other.
And the giant Simon Peter
ready to become a leader of men.

> *My brothers!*

Jesus' voice was rich.
Hit through to the core of their beings.
And so filled with life.
And hope.

> *I will teach you to be fishers –*
> *fishers of men.*

And He was off,
running ahead of them.

And like young boys,
whooping and shouting,
filled with knowledge
and yet utterly innocent,
the fishermen raced after Him.
And over the distant hills,
the sun broke.
And a new day dawned.

*Come to me my Lord.*
*Speak to me in the wonder of creation.*
*Intrigue me in the mysterious.*
*Challenge me through friendships.*
*Inspire me through learning.*
*Love me through others.*
*And call me*
*ever closer,*
*as I follow Your way*
*in this world –*
*and the next.*

Sunset on the estuary
*Watercolour*

# The Dance

They had started off with such high spirits.
Teasing and arguing.
Miriam had held hands with her friends
as they ran ahead down the lanes.
Excitement filled the air.
Expectation.
Promise.

But the heat that day was intense.
It wore down even the most exuberant.
Long before reaching their destination parents were exasperated,
tempers had become frayed.
Miriam had become silenced by the irritability,
wanted to go home.
And Hannah, her little sister,
was being impossible;
fractious and crying when she had to walk,
arching her back and screaming when carried.
Miriam knew her mother was at the end of her tether.

They'd been told *just round the corner* so many times
that it was a real surprise when they arrived.
Fields of green, deep, waving grasses,
people milling around.
Everyone busy.

They were pointed towards a group of men.
Talking in a tight knot,
their faces grave and serious.
One of them was frowning.
The grown-ups with them became edgy, nervous.
Miriam held Hannah's hand tightly.

*I'll ask.*

Miriam's mother went forward and tapped the shoulder of one of the men.
He turned and listened to her,
then looked round at the cluster of children and parents.

He spoke to another man
and both of them came to where they waited.

> *I'm sorry. Jesus is busy at the moment.*
> *Another time maybe.*

Miriam saw her mother's tired face flush red with the rebuff.

> *We've come a long way to see him,* she started to say.

> *No. It's a really bad time.*
> *Tomorrow perhaps.*

The men started to gently shoo them away.
Miriam felt an awful burning inside.
Her mother's face had turned almost scarlet.
Somehow, these men had made her mother look small.

> *Doesn't Jesus want to see us?* whispered Hannah.

> *I think he's too busy.*

Her mother didn't speak.
Miriam knew that look.
When you wanted to cry, but you couldn't
because everyone was looking at you.

The pain shot inside her.
She longed to wrap her arms around her mother
and take her away from these men,
soothe away the beaten look of humiliation,
bring back her loveliness
now blotched under scalding cheeks.

*O Jesus! If only you knew,* she whispered.
*Jesus, please see us.*

They'd reached the edge of the field
the parents silently gathering the children
to help them over the fence,
when suddenly a voice was heard,
the sound of running feet –
and all the children turned as one.

They knew.

There could only be one man who would run towards
them with His arms open wide.

Screaming and shouting
they raced to Him.
Feet flying
arms reaching up into His embrace.
Laughing,
hugging
holding onto each finger and hand
and leg and scrap of garment they could reach.

Except for Hannah
who couldn't run as fast.
And Jesus saw her.
Holding on to the children on His back
and laughing aloud, He knelt down
so she could run straight into His arms.

*Well done little one.*

He gathered her to Him and rocked her.

*Who thinks they can catch me?*

He looked at them perfectly seriously,
but His eyes were dancing.

In the split second it took to draw breath,
He was gone.
For a moment no one moved.
Everyone stared, wide-eyed.

Even the grown-ups.
Miriam had never seen anything quite as beautiful.
Unlimited,
He leapt.
Weaving, soaring through grass and sky.
Quite exquisite.

Funny,
it was the youngest who understood first.
A great peal of child's laughter burst from Hannah
and she ran,
shrieking with delight, to join Him.

Miriam,
her limbs tingling to run with the others,
was aghast to see huge tears pouring down her mother's face.

*Mummy?*

Her mother caught her to her.

*Go darling!*

And suddenly everything that was wonderful filled her.
She thought her heart would burst with love
as she raced through the grass to catch His hand.
Laughing, He swung her into a dance.

*Get the grown-ups!* He called.

And with children streaming out around Him,
they raced back through the gathering,
catching hands,
setting the people dancing
until the whole crowd,
even the men who'd shooed them away
were somehow caught into this
wild and wonderful excitement.

And then it was all over.
They fell on top of Him,
exhausted, laughing, happier than they had ever been –
a hot mass of arms and legs and worn out children,
parents and men falling at His feet,
holding their sides and gasping for breath.

One of the very big men groaned as he lay flat out on the grass –

*Jesus, you're quite daft!*

Miriam felt Jesus laughing
that deep infectious laugh that comes from inside,
right from the heart;
felt it catch hold of her.
It struck her as terribly funny.
Unable to stop,
the giggles poured out of her,
growing and filling the air,
catching everyone,
until she couldn't sit up any more
and she fell over with her head on His chest.
Heard the wild racing of His heart.

As close to Him as she could get.

Of course, eventually they had to go home.
No one wanted to.
They longed to hold onto these moments,
when the air was filled with golden flecks of dust,
and hovering insects turned into tiny gems in the setting sun.

Hannah lay fast asleep,
curled into the arms of their mother.
It really was time to go.

They left slowly,
Quiet goodbyes
echoing on the falling sky.

And suddenly Miriam wanted to say thank you.
She raced back up the field,

> *Jesus!*

He stopped and turned, holding His arms open to her.
Swung her up in the air.
Held her close.

> *I love you, Jesus.*

She held on to Him tightly,
wrapping her arms around His neck.

He held her tight.

> *I love you too my sweetheart.*

> *No –*
> *I will never forget,* she thought.
> *Not even when I'm an old, old lady.*
> *I will always remember dancing with Jesus.*
> *Just the beginning.*
> She smiled.
> *It's just the beginning.*

*Teach me to dance, my God.*
*And let the weariness drop away*
*to feel the lightness beneath my heavy feet.*

*Teach me to dance, my God,*
*so I shall never lose*
*the gift of child-like trust.*

*Teach me to dance, my God,*
*so, as I grow more care-filled,*
*I can discover life more richly.*

*Teach me to dance, my God,*
*so I may catch Christ's laughter*
*to share with lives I touch.*

*Teach me to dance.*

Spring Flowers, Mount Carmel
*Watercolour*

# The Giving

The dawn break came quietly
subtly changing the contours of light that lifted
around the foothills of Cana and whispered
between the sleeping streets.

The man stirred between sleep and visible reality
moving slowly through that strange time
when dreams merge with realised thoughts.
A time when God can move powerfully.

This was his marriage day.
Amongst the drifting dreams,
his heart beat quicker.

> *O God.*
> *So many emotions.*
> *I don't know where to begin.*

How could he even start to talk about the inexplicable wonder
of discovering that he loved someone?
How could he put into words the way he felt
when he watched her face reflect her thoughts?
How could he explain the sense of coming-home
when he was with her, or the feeling that at last he was made whole?
How could he possibly describe the delight of the future,
when he was also afraid?

His feelings and thoughts jostled amongst the fleeting dreams.

And then,
whilst still in the in-between,
he realised that God was there.
Closer than his own heartbeat.

God who already knew his delights and wonders and hopes;
already understood his fear.

And as he came to rest his life into God,
he realised that the hands that held him,
also held the dreams and fears of the woman he loved.

He opened his eyes to the day that was upon the house
and slowly smiled.

As the sun rose higher,
excitement swept through the village.
The joy of a wedding
began to sing in the air.

And gradually around the house of God,
the streets resounded with greetings and shouts
as old friends embraced and stories were remembered;
of expectation as the possibilities of new friendships murmured;
of mutual respect as the histories of two families came together.
And all this
because of the bond of love
between the woman and the man.

At the height of the celebration,
the steward of the feast approached the groom,
and discreetly indicated the empty flagons.
Embarrassment flushed over the wedding couple,
as they wondered how to tell their guests.
Yet within minutes, the steward was back at their side,
offering them the first taste of a new wine.
A look of surprise crossed the groom's face as he sipped it
before passing the cup to his bride;
together they listened attentively
as the steward indicated towards a group of guests.

Puzzled and not really taking everything in,
the couple stared at the group,
their eyes coming to rest on the carpenter.
And for a fraction of a moment,
the carpenter looked straight at them
with a look so full of laughter.
So full of life.
Startling.
So much so that they both caught their breath.

Taking his bride's hand,
the groom led the way through the ebullient guests to draw close to the man.
This could not be!
They were long-time friends.
Had played together, grown up together over the years.
Why – their families had known each other for ever!
The steward was simply telling a wild tale.

Yet – the proof was held in everyone's hands.
The deepest and reddest of wines.

He opened his mouth to speak,
but found he was completely confused.
Looking at someone he thought he knew well – he suddenly saw someone
totally different.
It must simply be a story.

But then the face he looked upon was so profoundly good.
And true.
And somewhere,
deep down,
deeper than all the delight and thrill of the day,
he felt a different excitement.
Something quite extraordinary had happened.
Today, of all days.

He frowned in concentration as he looked at his friend.
Feelings bound up in his marriage were also now, unexpectedly,
caught up with the carpenter.
He spoke slowly, with an awareness heightened
because of the emotions surrounding the day.

> *Today is all about giving, isn't it?*
> *To trust*
> *and to set free.*
> *But …*

He hesitated

> *… there is fear also.*
> *Because from today life changes.*
> *And great responsibilities lie ahead.*

He fell silent,
perplexed by his thoughts
yet aware that the carpenter was looking at him keenly.
It was strange.
As if his thoughts were already understood,
his feelings already shared,
the way ahead already opening.

> *We are at the beginning, aren't we?*
> *In different ways,*
> *on the brink of momentous journeys.*

The carpenter's smile deepened.
And His hands
rough and strong,
wrapped around theirs.

> *You are right, my friend.*

His grip tightened.

> *As for you,*
> *Heaven is rejoicing*
> *because of your love for each other.*

The hands held firm.
And the bride,
who had quietly watched and listened,
looked up into the carpenter's face
and spoke with absolute clarity.

> *You changed the water into wine.*
> *We do not understand how,*
> *maybe we never will,*
> *but we know it is a gift.*
> *For all to share.*

She hesitated, but the love in His face encouraged her on.

> *It's the changing of ordinary into special.*
> *Just as love has changed us.*

And she stopped.
For, as she looked at Jesus, she suddenly understood.

It was Love.
That extraordinary power,
force,
life-giver,
somehow embodied within the very being of the carpenter.

> *Jesus — thank you.*

Visible.
Tangible.
The alpha of all beginnings.

A gift.
For all.

And unstoppable.

Autumn in Brecon
*Watercolour*

| | | |
|---|---|---|
| *Love.* | *In Christ.* | *The greatest union.* |
| *Immeasurable.* | *In you.* | *The greatest venture.* |
| *Eternal.* | *In me.* | *Thanks be to love.* |
| *A revelation.* | | *Thanks be to God.* |

# Twilight

Nothing in the world prepared her for the news
or the look on the face of the speaker.
Her mind knowing
even before the words were said.
And then they were spoken.
And the world concaved.

> *We can do nothing to save him.*
> *He is going to die.*

From nowhere
a sword shot into her heart;
was out as quickly as it had come.
And suddenly she was back,
thirty-three years ago,
standing by the great pillars
in the Temple.
The sun drenching the stones,
the light in her eyes,
the hair wisping around her face.
Joseph, her darling Joseph, smiling at her,
as the old Temple-man leant forward to touch
the shawl edging the child's head.

And the baby,
heavy in her arms;
delicacy of the eyelids fast closed,
the tiniest of veins laid over them.
Perfection.

And the old man knew.
Knew about hope.
And knew about suffering.
Suffering beyond words.
And the compassion with which he spoke,
the tenderness as he looked into her eyes …

> … *and a sword will pierce through your soul also.*

The blackness of the present night swept over her.
She collapsed in the room,
her legs buckling as the coldest of winds rushed into her heart.

> *O God.*
> *Not my child.*
> *Not my child.*

Her mind raced for any kind of hope.
It could be they were mistaken.
They might have got the wrong person.
It simply was not possible that this most awful
of human tragedies was going to happen.
And it was going to happen to her.

For the rest of the night
she sat by the window.
Frantically giving her prayers to Him,
wherever he was in that silent city,

> *Don't give up my dearest.*
> *Don't give up.*

Around her
the faces were drawn.
Ashen in the lamplight.
Bewildered and afraid.

By dawn,
solid news arrived.
The Sanhedrin was assembling.

She pushed away the cloak they tried to put round her
and ran as fast as she could through the empty streets,
her heart threatening to burst with fear and agony.

> *O God – I've got to see him.*
> *I must see him.*

But it was too late.
The doors were closed.
He was already in the midst of it.

She leant against the wall,
the pain from running stretched across her face,
the colour draining.

> *Take her home,* one of the women whispered.

> *No!*

Her eyes flew open.
Fierce.

> *He's my child.*
> *I will not leave him.*

Within moments it seemed,
they heard the doors open.
A great swirling crowd of righteous men swept past them.
So quick.
She didn't even have time to call to Him.
Couldn't see him in the middle of the rapid convoy of guards and
Temple elders.
She looked desperately for someone to tell them where he had gone.

Pilate's.

She couldn't run anymore.
Leaned heavily on the women as they led her to the Governor's house.
She felt exhausted.
Spent.
By the time she got there,
the group had already left en route to Herod's residence.
Sickness rose within her.
Waves of fear and lack of sleep
kept sweeping over her.
She was vaguely aware
that they were going to stay there.
It seemed that Mary Magdalene thought he would be brought back.

But she knew.
Knew it deep inside.
The pain in her heart was so intense.
Her child was being put through hell.

>     *O God, help him.*

Knowing
yet not knowing.
If only she could support Him.
Everything in her closed off to the world
in order to hold him strong by sheer power of prayer.

She was brought back to the moment
by the rhythmic pounding of soldiers' feet,
the crowd stirring and straining.
The crowd.
She had no idea where they had all come from.
Hadn't even been aware of their gathering.

For a moment
her heart leaped.
They had come to get Him back,
to save Him.
And then her hopes fell.
She had seen this look on a crowd before.
An eagerness.
A presentiment of death.

She had to stop them.
She felt them move and swing in one direction.
Her eyes followed.

     *O God!* she gasped.

Her son had been brought to stand on the steps,
a cloak flung around his neck.
Even from a long way back,
she could see the jagged thorns knotted into His hair.
He could barely stand.

There was so much blood she had difficulty in recognising Him,
for his body had been assailed.

Her child.

The overwhelming horror held all the women in shock.
By the time she had pulled herself together,
the proceedings were underway.

The crowd was roaring,
Pilate was struggling to be heard.
The soldiers were getting angry,
pushing people back.

     *No! ... she called out ... No!*

But her cries were drowned.
People turned to look at her.
Someone laughed
   *– just a mother.*

She heard the sentence
amid the clapping and whistles of the crowd.

   *If only Joseph was still here,*
   *he'd have helped me to save him.*

And then they were moving.
The guard doubled.
Tight formation.
Crowd falling in behind.
The women pushed to the back.
Only the wailers, hungry for a spectacle, granted front position.
What right had they to be so close to her son?
They were strangers who had no love for Him
suddenly crashing in on his death.
Such anger inside.
They had no right,
no right to be there.

Somewhere,
up at the front,
her son was stumbling.
She quickened her pace.

   *He can't carry his cross –*
   *Oh God, how could they do this to him?*

The women with her pulled her back.

   *I won't see him humiliated like this.*
   *I will carry his cross.*

Mary Magdalene pulled her away.
Tears streaming down her face.

*You cannot carry his cross.*
*It is too heavy for any of us.*

She fought her off.

*I am his mother!* she cried.

And the terrible realisation of His death hit her.
The younger Mary took her back in her arms
and held her very close as she broke.
Huge awful sobs that wracked her body,
tearing the air around them.
On and on.

*He is my son and I have to watch him die.*
*There is nothing I can do.*

Nothing.
Except be there.

———

The crowd departed as soon as the crucifixion had taken place.
For the first time in all those nightmare hours,
the mother could see her son's face.
He was dying.
A slow and terrible death.

Anger such as she had never known blazed through her.

*What sort of God are you?*

She raged up at the glooming skies.

*What sort of God allows this to happen?*
*A God of love?*
*How can this be?*
*My child is dying.*

She searched the skies.

> I beg you
> not for my sake, not even for your sake,
> let him live.
> He was doing such good.

She started to plead.

> And he was only at the beginning.
> He is so desperately needed to carry on.
> You can't,
> you mustn't take him just yet.
> Take my life, Lord, but not my child's.

She waited for an answer,
but the air lay cold and heavy on her.
No pale sunlight glimpsed through the clouds.

> You could save him, she suddenly thought.
> Save from all this.
> Prove to everyone that you exist.
> Show your greatness.
> You saved the prophets and leaders of the past,
> so how much more reason to save your own child?

But there was no answer.
Her prayers lay suffocated about her.
No quiet reassurance in her heart.

> Then what has it all been for? she screamed.
> Why did you have me bring him into this world?
> You tell me the point.
> All those years in fear,
> in exile,
> living in a strange land off the kindness of foreigners,
> all the death and carnage that we left in our wake
> because of this child.

*What do I say now to those mothers whose children*
*were murdered at birth?*
*That it was because of this? This!*

She pointed to the cross,
silhouetted against the oppressive sky.

*Don't you dare not listen to me, God.*

The rage was firing her.
Keeping her alive.
Furious.
Her fists clenched and unclenched.
It was God's fault.

*It's not fair.*
*Why didn't you let Barabbas be picked?*
*Dear God, he was a killer.*
*What love or delight has he ever brought*
*into the world?*

And then a terrible thought struck her.

*Why my child?*
*Why not someone else's?*

There was an unbearable aching in the air.
As if hope was slipping away,
leaving an empty world behind.
She felt the tears well up inside.
And guilt.

Because she wished this horror was happening to
any child other than hers.

*I mean …*
*I don't want anyone to have to live through …*
*I didn't …*
*O God, help me.*
*Do not abandon me.*

She struggled to stay standing.
Couldn't tell whether it was the bleakness within her
that made the day seem so dark,
or if the heavens themselves were lowered with grief.

She watched His face.
So full of pain.
The colour of death slowly creeping over Him.

>    *O God,* she whispered.
>    *He is in such agony.*
>    *What am I doing willing him to live?*

She felt herself break inside.
There was no hope now.
She knew she had to let Him go.
She closed her eyes.

>    *I love him so much.*
>    *Help me, Lord –*
>    *for I don't know how to pray for my child to die.*

She could feel the awfulness of death.
The without.
The closing and dying within her own heart.
She knew,
as only one very, very close.
The end was imminent.

She walked forward,
past the waiting soldiers, into the death area.

Very gently she touched His feet.
And, just for a moment,
His eyes opened –
and He smiled at her,
the sweetest and most loving.
And then He was gone.

After,
there was nothing left to live for.
The emptiness enclosed her,
numbing her thoughts
and isolating her.
The greyness weighed her down,
each breath becoming a burden.

She longed to shut the world out;
to yield to the pain in her heart
and give up on life.

Let it quietly slip away.

But,
His people needed her.

The big-hearted men
who knelt down
and laid their heads into her arms as they wept;
the silent women withdrawn into nothingness,
staring ahead, unseeing.

All needing her.
The mother.
Never had she felt so old.
Never had she felt so tired.

And she,
who had been so close to God all her life,
now did not know how to pray.
She had no words left.

Mourning.
A place of utter desolation.
A twilight without dawn.
Seemingly unending.

So what news could this be,
carried by racing feet
and bursting voice,
as the light shafted over the mountain top?

In our world,
we too sit and watch death come to someone we love,
each in our own way so wracked with pain
that we do not know how to live.
For life,
absorbed without thought,
now hangs by such fragile threads.

I look at your fingers,
once so full of such potential,
now lying unmoving
within the hollow of your father's hand.
Exquisite.
But heartbreaking.

Maybe this is what is meant by love.
For we who love you are as one with you.
Walking this in-between world
until the time when you move on.

But it is such a desolate place.
Belonging to neither this world nor the next.
And we cannot live whilst watching you die.
Loneliness is etched around us.

And then,
in this transient place,
I become aware
that there is another.
Walking beside each of us.
Holding us all,
together,
with a force greater than earth and greater than death.

Hold us fast, Lord Jesus.
Hold us fast
until we, too, can see the dawn.

A. D. ASKEW

Windermere, Cumbria
*Watercolour*

# After

It was his own retching that woke him.
Brought him into the reality of the darkness.
For a long time he had no thought.
Just a terrible sense of unease.

> *O God.*
> *This was wrong.*
> *All wrong.*

As fragments of his life started to connect,
the unease grew into despair.
Something was missing.

There was heaviness all around him.
In him.
Pressing at him.
He reached out,

> *God, help me,* he whispered.

And suddenly it rushed in on him.
Stark and cold.
Tearing him apart.
He had no God.
He was the Betrayer.

> *No!*

His screams seemed to reverberate onto nothing.
Just emptiness.
Alone.
Of no belonging.
Even death had not stopped the pain.

> *O God, help me.*

His thoughts began to come clearer,
flowing into him.
He stirred,
pulled himself up so he could sit.

Here,
in this abandoned emptiness,
thinking was unconfined.
And that was frightening.
The power of thought.
Afraid, he tried to pull back,
but there was nowhere to go.

Whispered voices flittered around him.
Reasons, justifications, explanations.
There seemed so many of them.
Strong,
burning inside him.
Blatantly obvious.
Pushing him.
Driving him.
Forcing him to make the decision.

Here,
everything was different.
Perception was vast,
limitless.
He wondered if somewhere he had known of this
and closed it away –
because to look from here
was too threatening.
From here
he would have seen different possibilities.

Grief swamped him.
Sobs wracked him.

*What have I done?*

He covered his face with his hands.
Love and relationships,
fraught with misunderstanding, pain and misdirected intentions.

*I thought I knew him
I really believed I knew him.*

In this place,
the thought was preposterous.
Ridiculous.
How on earth could he possibly have believed
that he could have forced Jesus to act in a certain way.
How could he possibly have believed that his way was best?
How could he possibly have understood even a fraction
of Christ's mind?

It was overwhelmingly awful.
The outrageousness.
The stupidity.
The blinding refusal to look at life from any
angle other than his own.

Then he hauntingly remembered.
Christ looking at him.
Soul-filled.
The hurt.
The terrible grief of being betrayed by one you loved.

He heaved again into the darkness.

Sobs growing and suffocating him.

*I cannot live without you.*
*O Jesus – forgive me.*

His voice echoed into starless skies.

*I can't live without you.*

Hell.
The place without God.

He had no idea how long he was there.
Was it eternity?
But almost imperceptibly,
he became aware that the darkness was different.
Warmer.
Richer.
There was a Presence within it.

*Please?* he strained around.
*Please, God. Do not abandon me.*
*Do not leave me in this hell.*

All around him he felt the darkness sigh.
Was aware of the immeasurable weariness.
Exhaustion.
Eventually the reply came,

*Do not you, of all people, dare to speak of hell.*
*This is a hell of your own making.*

Memories shot through the dark.
Hit and sounded off him.
Infinitesimally
something resonated.

*Jesus?*

He couldn't remember.
Just couldn't recall His voice.

But he felt the answer.
Jesus.
He breathed in.
A long, fluttering sob.

> *I'm so sorry.*

The silence grew.
He didn't know what to say but struggled to put
his words into the dark.

> *I thought I was being strong.*
> *So passionate, so militant.*
> *Yet I was the weakest one.*
> *Led into ways that closed you out.*
> *Shut me out from seeing the magnitude …*

He was having difficulty speaking.

> *… I was so intent on my way.*
> *I didn't know that you would be destroyed.*
> *I had no idea that you would …*

he floundered and went very quiet.

> *… maybe I did know.*

The silence was terrible.
And so very tired.
The voice was leaden.

> *The working of evil is very subtle.*
> *It plays on all human insecurities and lack of trust.*
> *You were corrupted by the closing of your mind*
> *to different ideas.*
> *Although evil is powerful —*
> *it was ultimately your choice, Judas.*

He felt terrified.
The awfulness of what he had done.
The enormity.

*That's why I had to die.*
*It was the only choice left.*

Immediately he sensed a difference.
Anger.
Real anger surrounding him.
The words were furious.

*Tell me, Judas –*
*why do you think birth is so hard?*
*So full of risk?*
*A time when pain and beauty tear each other?*

The darkness seemed to be sparking.
He felt bewildered.
Judas didn't understand what he had said,
or why the talk had suddenly turned.

*The gift of life is not easily given.*
*It is created through great sacrifice.*
*Great love.*

There was a tremendous roaring inside his head.

*Do you know how many of my children would*
*long to hold their father, their child, their wife,*
*for just one day longer?*
*Do you know how many of those riddled with disease,*
*wake each morning thanking God for another day on earth?*
*Do you know the pain of watching death snatch away lives*
*of such promise?*
*How **dare** you hold this precious life so cheap,*
*you, who had so much.*

Fear held him bound.


Something was yawning before him that he had
hitherto not seen.
The possibilites within life.

The largeness.
The hugeness.
The wonder.

> *But …but … he cried back,*
> *I had nothing to live for.*

> *You had everything.* The reply ripped into him.
> *Everything, Judas.*

> *No!!*

His scream wrenched his soul out and he fell,
curled into a tight ball, his arms wrapped over his head.

The Presence spoke more quietly.

> *The power of good is always stronger than the twisting of evil.*
> *Did it never occur to you,*
> *that if you had lived and sought forgiveness,*
> *God could have worked great things through you?*
> *Think a while on those thoughts, Judas.*

Life as it could have been.
Betrayal.
Redemption.
Coming together in his person.
A new gospel.
Forgiveness.

He lay in the dark.
Empty.

> *I should have had the courage to stay, Lord.*
> *Begun anew.*
> *Maybe it would have been possible.*

*Judas, there are always different choices.*
*Death is not one of them.*
*Death is one of life's certainties.*

He knew he had to get the final words out.

*I put you to death, Lord.*
*I stopped all that you could have done.*

It was over. Finished.
Nothingness complete.


But then he felt the smile in the voice,
long before he heard it.

*Oh no, Judas. Death cannot stop me.*
*Even through the greatest evil, God **will** overcome.*
*Death —*
*and life —*
*are changed forever now.*

And then he saw that which he thought he had lost forever.
Light.
Rippling around, above, below him.
Touching him.
Absorbing him.
Warming the numbness.
Filling the emptiness within and without.


He didn't understand what Christ meant.
But the light was real. He looked up.
Deep into its source.
Felt the words.
And held on to them.


*There is a long way to go, Judas,*
*and there is so much to talk about …*
*Now come,* commanded Christ,
*It is time.*

*How can I condemn*
*when I am guilty of betrayal too?*
*The betrayal seen in a thousand glances,*
*cast in a thousand thoughts,*
*committed in a thousand ways.*

*It is a feeling of terror*
*to recognise the Judas that hides in me.*
*For in the recognition*
*a hopelessness creeps in.*
*Slowly deadens,*
*cloying all I am and could be.*
*Until I am shut out.*
*Alone.*
*Watching from a distance*
*as the rich tapestries of life unfold without me.*

*O my Christ.*
*How I need you to break the hell that I have made.*
*Come and find me, Lord, I beg,*
*and lead me back,*
*for without you I cannot find the way.*
*Only you can bring me home.*
*Only you.*
*My true, unfailing friend,*
*my God.*

Full Tide
*Watercolour*

# Unbelief

He didn't believe them.
It was as simple as that.

Watching them,
there was no doubt that some strange,
unexplained occurrence
had happened.
He was not one to dwell on the complications of the mind,
but he was also no fool.
He understood that thought focused into prayer
was an immensely powerful force.
And, after three years with Jesus,
he had become used to being opened
to depths and complexities of thought-fields
beyond human conception.
And he was all too aware of how the mind could play tricks.
He had seen many people led into bizarre beliefs by false prophets,
sometimes whole communities convinced of strange phenomena.

Maybe this was what was happening here.
A community, distraught with grief and longing,
had created an illusion.

But then,
they lived in an age of mirages.
And Christ was too real,
too solid,
too human
to appear, even in the mind, as an illusion.

It was all very difficult.
They were his closest friends.

When you lived Christ together,
you loved and cared as immediate family.
But now, as he watched them,
he felt turmoil inside.
Troubled by their transformation.
And deeply envious that, despite their efforts,
it did not rub off on him.
In fact,
it drove him further into isolation.
And being alone heightened the pain of grief.

And guilt.
Because he couldn't step where they had gone.

He wanted proof.

> *You want me to believe, God?*
> *Then send me Jesus.*

There had to be reason
in order to have faith.
If only he could see the tangible evidence,
then he could believe.

There was just no precedent.
Words had been spoken.
But words were words.
A resurrection was deed.
The arguments went over and over.

And then he remembered Lazarus.

> *O God.*

This was so complicated
and different
and shattering.
He buried his head in his hands.

It needed faith.
And he couldn't do it.
Couldn't move forward.

It made him speak more angrily.
Trying somehow to dampen their radiance.
Saying things he would have kept private.

It had been just after dawn
when the men had brought the news.
The tomb was empty.
Sickening thought.
Even in death Jesus wasn't left in peace.
The plotting of the Sanhedrin
turned his stomach over.

But no one had been prepared for Mary Magdalene.
Never one for the discreet,
she had terrified them with the noise of her feet,
the doors flung open,
her unstoppable bursting excitement.

She'd seen Jesus!

Laughing and talking,
her hair falling over her face,
the women clustering around her,
catching her vivacity.
She knelt beside Jesus' mother.
Gently kissing away her tears.
The older Mary holding on to her.
Her eyes startled, full of hope.
Trusting her.
Believing her.

The men too had gathered round.
Listening,
then exchanging glances.
Pitying her.
Quietly moving away.
Infuriating her with their refusal to believe.

Funny.
It was the women who drew her back to them.
Repeating the dawn story again and again,
their hands intertwined,
their faces changing with light and impossibilities.
And belief.

He had had to slip out that evening,
so he left under cover of darkness.
After Peter had been recognised,
none of them dared show their face in public.
Their friends brought them food and the latest news.

The authorities were very edgy.
Arrest first and question later.

He had stopped at the corner of the street on the way back.
He didn't think that anyone had noticed him.
He had stepped quietly into the shadowed archway –
and stopped short.
He had left in blanket silence and darkness
but now the courtyard was alive –
light tumbling down onto it,
noise and shouting pouring out of the windows.

Matthew ran past,
skidded to a halt and grabbed him.
Laughing, breathless, pushing him up the stairs,

*What's happened?*
*What's going on?*

They were completely different.
Giddy, wild, exhilarated.

*Jesus! Here – he was here!*

*Alive! We've seen him!*

He had stared at them bewildered
and they had clapped their hands in delight
and laughed at his astonishment.
Perplexed, he sat down.
All of them trying to tell him at once.
Stunned.
Unable to take it all in.
Over and over and over again,
they each swore to him that Jesus had appeared.
Exasperated, they couldn't understand
why he couldn't believe them.

He felt sick inside.
They were all so expectant of him,
waiting for him to be as delighted,
as eager as they were.
He just couldn't do it.
Could not ultimately believe that Jesus really had come back.
He felt utterly and desperately alone.
Grief threatening to pour down his face.
Suddenly red-hot, furiously angry with them.
That's why he'd talked about putting his hand
into the spear gash in Jesus' side.
So brutal.
So hard.
Anything to shut them up.

And now the days were running on.
It didn't look like Jesus was coming back again.
He cursed himself repeatedly.
Why, oh why, had it been that moment when he was
away, that they had apparently seen Him?
If only he had been there,
he could have stopped this nonsense.
Brought them to their senses.
And yet,
at the same time,
he yearned to believe them.
His heart ached to see Jesus,
to hear His voice,
to laugh with Him.
And they were so
immensely
alive.
Alive with sheer happiness.
The happiness that runs rich and warm,
holding the threads of life together,
that is the springboard from which we soar.

Sometimes,
listening to them,
his heart lifted strangely
and for a moment
he felt he was on the edge
and about to fly.
But then his mind pulled back.
Back into arguments.
Back into the need for proof.

Looking at them,
seeing their transformation,
wasn't proof enough.
He wanted more.

The dark began to fall
and lamps were lit.
He shut the door himself,
double-checking the bolts.
Climbed wearily into the upper room,
locked now into his own thoughts,
sat and closed his eyes.
Slowly became aware that the
conversation had stopped.
An incredible sixth sense of everyone holding their breath.

He glanced up
and his heart thumped through his ribcage.
Jesus was standing right in front of him.
No one spoke.
Even Simon Peter had gone white with the shock.
Thomas scrambled to his feet.
He was so real.
Really there.
Warm flesh and blood.

Jesus looked around the room.
Saw their amazed,
frightened,
hope-filled faces.

> *Peace my friends!* He murmured,

and instantly everyone let out tightly-held breaths,
and started grinning at each other,
shuffling with the easing of tension.

Jesus turned back to Thomas who was still
rooted to the floor.

> *Thomas, my friend.*
> *How many people, best friends, brothers, sisters,*

*do you need to tell you the truth*
*before you have faith to believe?*

He held out His hand.

*Come –*
*put your finger into these holes in my palms,*
*slide your hand in here – deep into my side.*
*Is that what you really need*
*in order to believe?*

Thomas felt the tears well up inside,
brimming over, running down his face.

*My Lord.*
*My God,* he whispered.

And Christ smiled. Just for him.
Slow and deep and understanding.

*Blessed are those who have not seen me –*
*and still believe.*

His eyes did not move from Thomas' face.
And immediately Thomas knew.
Knew what was being asked of him.
Where his ministry would lie.
For who better than he,
who knew the despair of lack of faith,
to give the rest of his life to those who could not believe?

And at that moment
the nailed hands touched his face.
Suffering embodied
in its myriad forms.

Thomas placed his hands over Christ's.
Felt his heart soar.
And, stepping forward, in absolute belief,
he smiled up into the face of God.

I do understand how Thomas felt.
I too do not want easy platitudes
nor pious reassurances,
however kindly meant.
I too
have longed for living proof.

But then,
very, very slowly
I have come to realise
that the tangible is a world far apart from belief.
And faith
is the slow and startling discovery of you, God, in Christ.
Quietly waiting.
Deep, deep
within my heart.

Last Light, Arrochar
*Watercolour*

# Holding Fast

Stephen stretched his legs out in front of him
and leant his head back against the wall.
Felt the warmth of the sun
spread along his back
and down his shoulders.
He smiled.
These were wonderful days.

To his eyes,
it seemed that since the Resurrection
the city had become bathed in a glorious glow.
He wondered if that was so –
or could it be that he was so changed by Christ
that he saw life differently,
maybe as God had always intended it to be?
The streets were just as crowded,
the everyday still had to be faced –
yet everywhere one could sense
a tremulous air of expectation.
He could only describe it as a time of transformation,
an amazing opening of hearts to God.
Such a fierce and joyous burgeoning.

Thinking about the everyday
brought his thoughts back to this day – and he sighed.
Within this time,
caught into these world-changing events,
you would have thought that celebrating Christ,
living for the Christ,
would be straightforward.
But human nature was unbelievably precarious.

The congregations were overflowing,
there was such a yearning to hear of Christ,
but sometimes
people became hurt,
especially if they felt slighted or ignored –
or lonely –
within such a vast group of people.
Often it was the most insignificant remarks
that could develop into deep rifts,
souring and disillusioning.
He could not bear to see that happen.
That was why the apostles had appointed him, alongside others,
to ensure that the day-to-day practicalities ran smoothly.

The people said the Holy Spirit moved within him,
but he wasn't aware of that.
He just knew that his heart delighted in God
and, basing his life on Christ,
he tried to deal compassionately with all.

Today though had been trying.

Yet again representatives from different synagogues
had argued and harangued him
in front of the people.
Trying to belittle him.
And mock Christ.
Sometimes he had to constantly remind himself
of Christ's face
to deal courteously with such aggression.
That was why this time of quiet,
back at home, whilst waiting for supper,
helped to put the jealousies into perspective.

The warmth of the sun-baked stones crept
over him and his eyes closed.
Despite everything
it was a wonder-filled time to be alive.
He wouldn't have missed it for the world.

The crash of a door slammed him awake.
It took him a moment,
surfacing from sleep,
to register the voices raised in anger.

A sharp cry from his wife
and he was running –
across the courtyard,
down the corridor.
Cries of fear,
the thudding of many feet.
Chaos.
Screams.

He burst into the foyer –
and stared in total disbelief.

His wife was kneeling on the floor
her hands desperately trying to staunch the blood
that flowed from his servant's head;
hired guards were everywhere,
packing the hallway,
spilling threateningly into the rooms.
Temple elders and scribes clustered importantly
in the doorways.

Suddenly face to face with him they hesitated.
For a moment,
with the servant and woman on the floor,
they looked shame-faced before brazening,

*The Council wants you.*
*We've questions to ask.*

In the stillness,
he was aware of his wife's startled glance.

His voice,
normally deep and slow,
burnt with anger.

*You only had to ask and I would have come.*
*Do not ever again*
*come into my home with open swords.*

A guard moved to seize him
only to find himself stepping back,
momentarily daunted by the blaze of anger.

Stephen knelt heavily beside his servant
and met his wife's eyes.
Strange how a look can change everything.
Her face at that moment was exquisite –
for it was filled with love.
A love that comes from the richness of memories,
a life together.
A love that was beyond words.
The deepest and the most endless.
And breaking across that love, came fear –
and a terrible realization.
And he felt his heart turn within him.

He held his hand to her face and she caught his fingers.

And then he was gone.
And she knew.

As they travelled the short distance to the Council,
he could feel the difference in the air.

The sun was dropping,
and the streets were draughty.
A shiver ran across him.

He was still seething with anger as they
jostled him through the great doors.
Before he had time to take in what was happening,
a man he had never seen before began to speak,
spinning a tale of outrage against him.
Looking around in bewilderment,
it seemed as if there was a tingling of madness in the air.

This was a trap.
Everyone in the Sanhedrin was present.
All waiting for him. But why?

What was it all about?
And why had they come for him?

He listened more carefully.
And suddenly he realised.
They were attacking the Church.
He had been picked because he had a high
profile among the local leaders.
His stomach churned inside.
What was he on trial for?
The accusations being brought against him could carry the death penalty.
This was deadly business.

He felt himself swaying and pulled himself up.
Somewhere, someone must be on his side.
But the faces stared back at him filled
with venom and hatred.
Fear was making him sick.
By the time the bribed liars had finished,
he would stand for nothing.

His only way out would be to denounce Christ.
Denounce Christ.
The Jesus he had laughed with and shared bread with;
the Jesus he loved more than anyone;
the Jesus he knew he would always stand for.

How could he possibly denounce Him?
He was at the centre of his heart.
The reason for his being.

He suddenly felt desperately, terribly alone.
Where were the others?

> *O God help me.*

And then, quite clearly, it came to him.

> *Why – Jesus stood here*
> *in this very place,*
> *maybe on these very stones.*
> *Faced these same closed minds.*
> *The way has been trodden before.*
> *I am not alone. I am **not** alone.*
> *Hold me Jesus.*

He breathed Christ in deeply.
His shoulders went back and, unbeknown to him,
his face shone, like that of an angel.

> *My brothers,* he began,

and his voice resounded around the hall.

> *Fathers of this nation,*
> *you accuse me of traitorous actions*
> *against you and God,*
> *so now listen to what*
> *I have to say.*

And he knew the words to speak.
They flowed from him.
Inspired.
Reminding them of their history and the
men of faith from Abraham to their great leaders;
reminding them of how evil worked,
using oppression
and jealousy
and internal squabbling;
reminding them that they themselves stood in a line
of power-seekers who repeatedly shut out the Holy Spirit.

> *Like fathers, like sons.*

His voice thundered on,
uncomfortably jolting into their memory the deaths of the prophets,
stirring guilt and shame
and unknowingly fuelling the evil
that was waiting for the exact moment.


His fear had gone.
He felt Christ very close to him.
He was more alive now than he had ever been.

> *And you!*

He spun round, his eyes missing no one.

> *What did you do when your turn came?*
> *Did you stand by the God you preach of?*
> *Did you hold to the commandments you force upon others?*
> *No?*
> *Why not?*

The air seemed to crack with the tension.

> *You betrayed!*
> *At the deepest level human thought and action can sink to.*
> *You became murderers –*
> *of the Son Of God.*

His anger pounded through them.
And though he was aware of the hatred
lashing around him,
he felt strangely up-held.
As if for a moment,
he was a giant of faith.

He looked up and beyond and unwittingly laid himself open to death.

For he looked straight up into the face of God
and, unable to contain himself,
his heart bursting with delight,
he cried out,

> I see heaven! And the Son of Man standing at the right hand of God ...

It was the pivotal moment of blasphemy
that they were waiting for.

It all happened so quickly that he didn't even
feel the impact as he hit the floor,
his sight of heaven lost in a stampede of kicking feet.
Shouts and screams and blows hit into him
as they caught his arms and legs.
Unable to shield himself,
he was dragged across the flagged floor,
all thought vanishing in a terrified daze
as his head struck stones.
The rush of cold air outside,
the startled gaze of onlookers,
the noise thundering in his ears,
the men gathering pace,
the grunt as they swung him –
and then,
for a long moment,
silence
as his body fell in free fall.

He hit the ground with a dull thud.
Even before his body had stopped sliding
they were already running towards him,
their hands scrabbling in the dirt for stones.

As in all hunts,
the most bestial closed in to watch.
One especially stood out,
his eyes glittering with the sight,
imprinting it onto his mind.

A man whose name was Saul.

As the stones rained into him with increasing force,
Stephen knew that everything in him was dying.
And, at that moment, everything within him fought to live.
Pain shattered his sight.

> *Where is God?*
> *O God, do not abandon me,*
> *do not leave me now …*

He forced his head up and opened his eyes –
and his heart filled overwhelmingly.
For there,
right in the middle of that terrible volley
of death stones
was Christ,
running towards him,
His arms open wide.

Somehow
his broken body struggled up
and he tried to run to his Lord,
but his legs were snapped
and he fell
sprawling,
into the dirt.

     *Wait for me, my Lord,*

he whispered,

     *I'll be with you in a moment.*

And then he realised
that Christ was beside him,
kneeling in the filth and the blood.
And he felt Christ's arms wrap strong and sure about him.
Looking up into the face he knew so well,
Stephen whispered,

     *Do not hold it against them.*

And Christ smiled.
That smile
of the most powerful love.
A love beyond all human force.

     *My true servant.*

He gathered him up into His arms,
carrying him high above the power of death.
And held him close,
very close,
against His own heart.

     *Come my friend.*
     *We are going home!*

*Jesus Christ.*
*The centre of my heart.*

*With your strength ...*

*I will stand for You*
*and walk tall with You.*

*I will work for You*
*and change the world with You.*

*I will love for You*
*and fill my days with You.*

*I will always be for You*
*and live my life with You.*

*Jesus Christ.*
*The centre of my heart.*

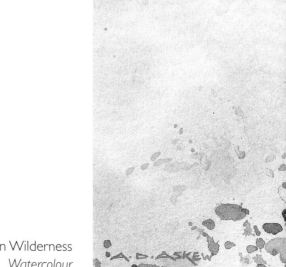

Masada, Judaean Wilderness
*Watercolour*

# Turning Point

The bloodying of Stephen
flashed again and again
onto the inside of his mind,
saturating his vision with red images.

His mind was brilliant.
His personality immensely forceful.
When he spoke in the synagogue,
all knew that it was traditional but clever.

In business he was never crossed.
That would be unthinkable.
For somewhere, where consciousness stopped,
and words had not formed,
there was an awareness,
an instinctive warning –
that this man, upholding the tight conventions of society,
was ruthless.

Almost,
a killer waiting for legitimacy.

This new religion enraged him.
It was blasphemous.
Wrong. Disturbing.
A threatening, seething anger built up inside him.

The redness of his thoughts
seemed to spread out and fill his body.
Watching the death of Stephen
had been fascinating.
Strangely exciting.

The pent-up energy within him had instantly focused.
It was all so clear.
This new religion, this Christ thing, must be stopped –
whatever the cost.

As the images repeatedly flickered,
justification came easily.
Legitimate. Emotive,
and best of all,
unarguable.

He was the one chosen to protect the holiness and sanctity of the faith.

The Sanhedrin were only too pleased to hand him authority,
for he was a powerful man
with formidable support from the traditionalists.
His was the mind that was needed to spearhead the campaign,
and to absolve them of blood guilt.

Saul glittered inside.
His thoughts were highly channelled,
devising plans and strategies for the immediate
quelling of this heresy.

Adrenalin pumping,
hands sweating,
the soldiers waited for the command.
Saul watched as the door went crashing down.

They were in,
children flung to one side,
orders clear –
adults only for the moment, including servants and women.
He could hear the simultaneous raid on the house
in the street next door.

Screams and shouts filled the air.
People running,
the noise of soldiers' pounding feet,
the sharp cry as someone fell,
the shocked stares of neighbours.

Within minutes it was over.
Fast and furious.
Highly successful.
And so very easy.
For they were unprepared, bewildered,
terrified by the noise and sudden brutality.

Of course, this was just the beginning.
The others would be warned and harder to find.

But he would find them.
Oh yes.
He would find them all.

Within days
the Christ followers were scattered.

Homes abandoned as the people disappeared.
The glorious aura of the Church's beginnings smashed and broken;
the golden trembling of birth
shot through with tears, pain, blood.
And everywhere
a name whispered.
A name synonymous with torture and death.
The name of the mastermind.

Saul.

Jerusalem was stamped into submission.
Instantly he lost interest in the city.

There was much to do
and so little time.
The status quo must not,
**must not**, he thought fiercely,
be challenged.

He waited in the chambers for the papers to authorize
his hunt further afield into Damascus.
The High Priest
avoided his eyes.
Even he,
in his high appointed office, was afraid of him.
Saul despised him.
How could the faith be kept safe in hands like his?
Weak men,
hiding behind ritual and position.
It needed people like himself,
who understood the balance between
legitimacy and violence to ensure that their ancient faith remained pure.
Unsullied.

The heat of the day lay in waves across the road.
Jerusalem shimmered behind him.
Reality merged with mirage.
He strode on,
pushing his servants and soldiers,
through the midday sun,
determined that the fleeing heretics would not damage
society's infrastructure.
And suddenly he realised
the extent of his power.

He had become untouchable.
It was an immensely pleasing thought
and he found himself secretly smiling.

There was no distant thunder.
No clouding of the sky.
No warning.
A light more brilliant than human eye could stand broke over him.
Piercing.
Devastatingly searing.
Intensity of heat.
Whiter than anything seen in nature.
An iron held in the heart of the fire awaiting transformation.

No beauty.
No glory.
Scouring.

Saul dropped like a stone, his hands clutched to his eyes,
gasping within the blinding.
And into the middle of the pain a voice spoke,

> *Saul, Saul.*

A voice of incredible gentleness.
And so full of brokenness.

> *Why are you persecuting me?*

Saul froze.
Not a voice he recognised.
None of his servants, nor the captain of the soldiers, spoke like that.
His thoughts were racing inside the glare.
Could it possibly be one of the victims?
Surely not.

But whoever it was was standing very near to him.
Close enough to touch.
He spun round, trying to gauge where it had come from.
Fear pumping through him, born from self-knowledge,
for this was an encounter with power on a magnitude beyond
anything human.

*Who are you, Lord?* he queried.

*I am Jesus.*

For a second his heart literally stopped with shock.

He found himself,
the great unassailable one,
completely blank,
whimpering,
waiting for the lash of vengeance.

But it didn't happen.
The light intensified.
The voice continued.
And only then, as he struggled to grasp at chaotic thoughts,
did he hear the most terrible sound.
The sound of a heart breaking.

*Why are you persecuting me?*

Echoing on.

And instantly,
without him wanting it to,
his mind recalled
every face,
every home,
every child dragged screaming from their parents,
every sob,
every look,
every broken body.

*Jesu Christus.*

Twisting in crucifixion.

*O God.*
*O my God.*

The realization was terrifying,
as the whole foundation of his life,
his entire belief, the absolute certainty of his religion,
collapsed inside him.

Unaware of being led by his servants
to his original destination,
the days passed by.

Locked outside time,
his sight turned inwards,
his mind hurtled down chasms of thought.

He had blindly looked into the face of Christ.
He had encountered the undeniable Son of God.
Concepts.
Ideologies.
Doctrines.
Creeds.
Structures.
Life-long securities.
All floundered between disbelief and growing despair.

Desperately seeking foundation,
his mind caved and swerved,
discovering every nook,
every cranny,
every established firm-hold
had dissolved into chaos.

If Christ was the Son of God,
what atrocities had he, Saul, committed —
and in the name of God?

The faces haunted him.
Scenes of awfulness.

One especially was etched deeply into his subconscious.
Again and again he saw Stephen falling,
again and again he saw the way his arm had bent,
again and again that most sickening of sights,
his hand lying wide open,
fingers slightly curled amongst the debris of death.

> *Oh Lord.*
> *I'm so sorry.*
> *I'm so sorry.*
> *How can you ever forgive me?*

The tears scorched,
destroying and cleansing at the same time,
burning the inside of his eyes.
Finally escaping,
they trailed down his ravaged face.

And then,
in amongst the scalding heat
he felt cool fingers moving.
Strange hands
that tenderly healed.
Slowly lifting away the sightlessness.

Almost imperceptibly,
he realised that a man was standing in
front of him.
But it was so confused an image that he had
difficulty deciphering it.

> *Stephen?*

He touched the face,
his fingers travelling down to the man's hands,
turning them over and over,
gazing in wonder,
holding them close to his sight,

absorbing the creases,
the work-stained fingers,
the broken nail.

And he knew that he was forgiven.
He gave a great worn-out sob and pressed
the hands to his face.

And the Christ-follower,
who had come in obedience to God's call,
watched and waited and understood.

Gradually,
Saul realised that this was not Stephen,
but a stranger.
And yet,
there was something about him that he recognised.

> *What is it that is so familiar in your face?*

he finally asked.

And the follower smiled.

> *We have all been touched by Christ.*
> *Love transforms us …*

And his smile deepened,

> *… as it does you.*

Love.
That was it.
Love that held the dynamic forces of this world together
and created all that was seen and unseen.
Love that was confined into man
and broke the ultimate bond of death to set us free.
Love that was bound into the deepest suffering
and the greatest joys.

Love that was the beginning and the end.
The Eternal that had come for him.
And brought him home.

The Christ-follower moved to the doorway
and turning back,
held out his hand.
A surprisingly warm and genuine human offering.

And, for a fleeting moment,
it seemed that another hand reached out.
The hand of Christ.
Worn and beautiful and strong.

Saul,
who was to become Paul,
walked forward and placed his hand
into the hand of the follower.

>  *There is so much I want to live for.*
>  *So much I have to share.*

The cold air of the morning lifted the
noise of the city to them.
Life held such potential,
such excitement,
such goodness,
such adventures.

He breathed in deeply at the wonder of life
and then flung his head back to the sweeping skies.

>  *Christ …*
>  *I am yours!* he cried.

And, as his great heart filled with love,
he stepped out
into the waiting world.

*What God is this –*
*who is seen so visibly*
*within the chaos of my unruly life?*

*What God is this –*
*who quietly speaks into my heart*
*when I have nothing of loveliness left within?*

*What God is this –*
*who enters into my darkness*
*to tenderly search my face?*

*What God is this –*
*who opens my unseeing eyes*
*and holds His arms to me?*

*My God –*
*who comes to me.*
*I who am the least.*
*Healing my heart.*
*Filling my being with the power and the glory of*
*abundant love.*

*Amen I say to my God!*
*In the name of my Christ,*
*Amen and Amen.*

Galilee, Sunrise
*Watercolour*

# The Leprosy Mission Contact Addresses and Telephone numbers

TLM International
80 Windmill Road
Brentford
Middlesex TW8 0QH
United Kingdom
Tel: 020 8326 6767
Fax: 020 8326 6777
friends@tlmint.org
www.leprosymission.org

TLM Trading Limited
PO Box 212
Peterborough PE2 5GD
United Kingdom
Tel: 0845 1662253
Fax: 01733 239258
enquiries@tlmtrading.com
www.tlmtrading.com

TLM Africa Regional Office
PostNet Suite # 280
Private Bag X844
0127 Silverton
Republic of South Africa
Tel: 00 27 12 349 2406/7
Fax: 00 27 12 349 2406
email: lep.afr@inter.nl.net

TLM Australia
PO Box 293
Box Hill
Victoria 3128
Tel: 61 39890 0577
Fax: 61 39890 0550
tlmaust@leprosymission.org.au
www.leprosymission.org.au

TLM Belgium
PO Box 20
Vilvoorde 1800
Tel: 32 22519983
Fax: 32 22519983
leprazending@online.be

TLM Canada
75 The Donway West
Suite 1410
North York
Ontario M3C 2E9
Tel: 1 416 4413618
Fax: 1 416 4410203
tlm@tlmcanada.org
www.tlmcanada.org

TLM Denmark
Spedalskhedsmissionen
Peter Bangs Vej 1 D
DK - 2000 Frederiksberg
Tel: 45 3838 4888
Fax: 45 3887 1493
lepra@lepra.dk
www.lepra.dk

TLM England & Wales,
Channel Islands &
Isle of Man
Goldhay Way
Orton Goldhay
Peterborough PE2 5GZ
United Kingdom
Tel: 01733 370505
Fax: 01733 404880
post@tlmew.org.uk
www.leprosymission.org.uk

TLM Finland
Hakolahdentie 32 A 4
00200 Helsinki
Tel: 358 9 692 3690
Fax: 358 9 692 4323
eeva-liisa.moilanen@kolumbus.fi

TLM France
18, rue Justin
92230 Gennevilliers
Tel: 33 1 4794 6776
pierregeiser@wanadoo.fr
www.leprosymission.org

TLM Germany
Küferstrasse 12
73728 Esslingen
Tel: 49 711 353 073
Fax: 49 711 350 8412
LEPRA-Mission@t-online.de
www.lepramission.de

TLM Hong Kong
8b South Bay Towers
59 South Bay Road
Hong Kong
Tel: 852 2812 6435
Fax: 852 2812 7440

TLM Hungary
Alagi Ter 13
H-1151 Budapest
risko.marta@freemail.hu

TLM India Regional Office
CNI Bhavan
16 Pandit Pant Marg
Delhi 110 001
Tel: 91 11 371 6920
Fax: 91 11 371 0803
reception@tlm-india.org

TLM Italy
Via Adda 13
1 - 05100 Terni
Tel: 39 0744 811 218
agbertolino@librero.it

TLM Netherlands
Postbus 902
7301 BD Apeldoorn
Tel: 31 55 3558535
Fax: 31 55 3554772
leprazending.nl@inter.nl.net

TLM New Zealand
PO Box 10-227
Auckland
Tel: 64 9 630 2818
Fax: 64 9 630 0784
david.hall@tlmnz.org.nz
www.leprosymission.org.nz

TLM Nigeria
1 Ladi Kwali Road
off Paiko Road
PMB 179, Minna
Niger State
Tel: 234 66 224 840
Fax: 234 66 223 433
tlmnco@skannet.com

TLM Northern Ireland
Leprosy House
44 Ulsterville Avenue
Belfast BT9 7AQ
Tel: 028 9038 1937
Fax: 028 9038 1842
colinferguson@tlm-ni.org
www.tlm-ni.org

TLM Norway
PO Box 2347
Solli
Arbingst. 11N 0201
Oslo
Tel: 47 2243 8110
Fax: 47 2243 8730
gaute.hetland@
bistandsnemnda.no

TLM Portugal
Casa Adelina
Sitio do Poio
8500 Portimao
Tel: 351 82 471180
Fax: 351 82 471516
coaa@mail.telepac.pt

TLM Republic of Ireland
5 St James Terrace
Clonskeagh Road
Dublin 6
Tel: 353 1269 8804
Fax: 353 1261 3757
leprosymission2@eircom.net
www.leprosymission.ie

TLM Scotland
89 Barnton Street
Stirling FK8 1HJ
Tel: 01786 449 266
Fax: 01786 449 766
lindat@care4free.net
www.biggar-net.co.uk/
/tlmscotland

TLM South East Asia
6001 Beach Road
#08-06 Golden Mile Tower
199589 Singapore
Tel: 65 6 294 0137
Fax: 65 6 294 7663
ditch@tlmsea.com.sg

TLM Southern Africa
PO Box 46002
Orange Grove 2119
South Africa
Tel: 27 11 440 6323
Fax: 27 11 440 6324
peter@tlm.co.za

TLM Spain
Apartado de Correos
51.332 CP
28080 Madrid
Tel: 34 91 594 5105
Fax: 34 91 594 5105
misionlepra@lepra.e.
telefonica.net

TLM Sweden
Magasinsgatan 4
SE-692
37 Kumla
Tel: 00 46 19 583790
Fax: 00 46 19 583741
info@lepramissionen.org

TLM Switzerland
Chemin de Réchoz 3
CH-1027 Lonay/Vaud
Tel: 41 21 8015081
Fax: 41 21 8031948
mecl@bluewin.ch
www.lepramission.ch

TLM USA
American Leprosy Missions
1 ALM Way
Greenville
S C 29601
Tel: 1 864 241 1750
Fax: 1 864 271 7062
amlep@leprosy.org
www.leprosy.org

TLM Zimbabwe
PO Box BE 200
Belvedere
Harare
Tel: 263 4 741817
tlmzim@tlmzim.icon.co.zw